THE USBORNE

Write-in

NATURE

ACTIVITY

BOOK

Written by Emily Bone

Designed by Jamie Ball, Helen Edmonds,
Anna Gould and Tilly Kitching

Illustrated by Nat Hues, Samara Hardy,
Caroline Attia and Brian Fitzgerald

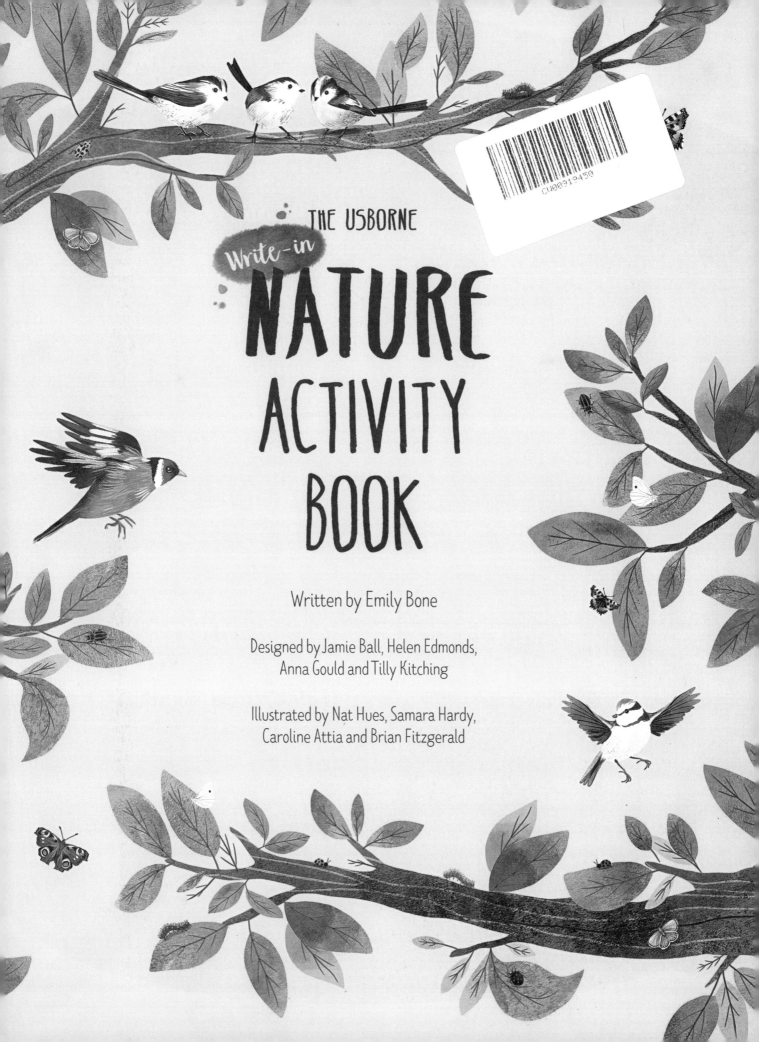

Nature activities

Grab a pen and tackle nature-themed puzzles, mazes, spot the difference, colouring in and much more. Learn all about different animals and plants too, from bugs in the garden, to turtles and dolphins in a tropical coral reef.

Usborne quicklinks

For links to websites with video clips, fun facts and activities about the animals and plants in this book, including ways to help the wildlife around you, go to

www.usborne.com/quicklinks

and enter the keywords 'nature activity book'.

Please follow the safety guidlines at the Usborne Quicklinks website.

Park puzzles

It's early in the morning, and only a few people are out and about in a city park. But lots of creatures have made the park their home, and they've been awake and busy for hours.

Animals to spot

Animals are tucked away in leafy trees and bushes, and lurking in the undergrowth in this picture. See if you can spot and circle these:

Four squirrels eating nuts
A fox with her three cubs
Eight yellow butterflies
A bird feeding its chicks
Two coots building a nest
Three sleeping raccoons
Two moles poking their heads out of the ground

4

Nesting boxes

A park warden has put up nesting boxes to encourage birds to lay eggs. He goes around every nesting box each week to check if any birds have moved in. He spends no longer than five minutes at each box and five minutes walking between each. Find the nesting boxes here and work out how long it takes the warden to check them all.

Time taken: ....

Nature trail

This map shows a nature trail around the park with the different areas and things to look out for.

Can you draw a route on the map for a visitor to see everything just once before leaving the park? The entrance and exit points are marked.

City Park map

Frog marsh

Wild flower meadow

Entrance

Canada goose green

Reptile scrubland

Old oaks

Exit

Pond

Memorial garden

Woodland trails

Eggs and nests

It's not just birds that lay eggs – all sorts of other animals do, too. See if you can match up nests to their animal owners, solve an egg Sudoku, find where a cuckoo has laid her egg, and take an egg-themed quiz.

Which nest?

Can you match up these nests to the animals that made them?

1.

2.

3.

4.

5.

A) Northern cardinal

B) Common frog

C) Salmon

D) Owl butterfly

E) Garden ant

Egg Sudoku

Different types of eggs have been collected to put in a display, numbered from 1-4. Fill the remaining boxes in this case, so each column, row and four-box section has an egg of each type.

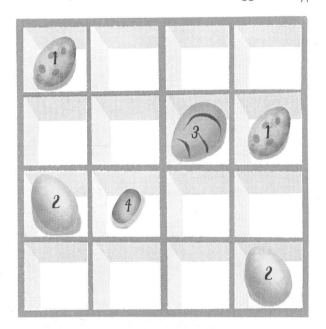

Biggest egg

The biggest eggs in the world are laid by ostriches. Each egg can weigh up to 1.5kg (3.3lbs) – as much as 30 chicken's eggs. The smallest are hummingbird eggs, which weigh less than 1g (0.03 oz).

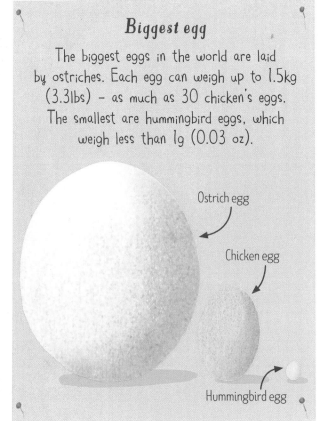

Ostrich egg

Chicken egg

Hummingbird egg

Find the cuckoo's egg

Cuckoos don't build their own nests. They lay their eggs in other birds' nests, so that when the chick hatches, those birds feed and look after it.

Cuckoos only choose nests with similar looking eggs to their own, but they never *entirely* match. Can you find and circle the cuckoo egg in one of these nests?

Are you an egghead?

Test your knowledge with these eggy questions:

1. Which of these animals DOESN'T lay eggs:

Duck-billed platypus

Grass snake

Crow

Koala

House spider

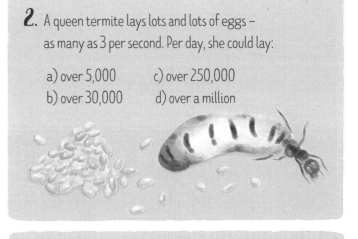

2. A queen termite lays lots and lots of eggs – as many as 3 per second. Per day, she could lay:

a) over 5,000   c) over 250,000
b) over 30,000   d) over a million

3. True or false? Sea catfish keep their eggs in their mouths, and the babies grow up there after they hatch.

TRUE/FALSE

Garden bugs

All kinds of bugs wriggle, crawl or fly around the undergrowth in
a garden. Some bury themselves deep underground, too.

Slug trail

A slug wants to slime its way to tasty strawberry plants on the other side of the garden. But a gardener has put down things to
stop it – slugs don't like crawling over spiky gravel or sharp nut and egg shells. Can you find a route for the slug to take?

Key:  Egg shells    Nut shells    Gravel

Going underground

Some baby bugs hatch from eggs underground. They live there for a *long* time before digging their way out and
turning into adults. The bugs here dug their way out in August 2018. Look at the length of time they
spent underground, then write down the month and year when each one hatched.

Cockchafer
2 years, 4 months

Cicada
17 years, 2 months

Stag beetle
6 years, 3 months

Crane fly
11 months

....

Bug trap

Someone has set up a bug trap to find out which bugs visit their garden. Using the flow chart below, can you identify the six bugs that have been caught? Write the correct number in the circle next to each bug.

Start here each time:

Does it have legs?

No / **Yes**

Does it have more than six legs?

Yes / **No**

Does it have a shell?

No / **Yes**

Does it have visible wings?

Yes / **No**

1. Snail
Snails hide inside their hard shells from animals that want to eat them. They leave slimy trails as they move.

2. Lacewing
Lacewings fly from flower to flower at night, feeding on the liquid inside, called nectar.

3. Earthworm
Earthworms have tiny hairs on their bodies to push their way through soil. They often come to the surface when it rains.

Does it have more than eight legs?

No / **Yes**

4. Shield bug
Also called stink bugs. When they're frightened, they squeeze out a smelly liquid from their legs.

5. Wolf spider
All spiders have eight legs. Wolf spiders use them to race after bugs they want to eat.

6. Millipede
Millipedes' long bodies are made up of lots of little segments, each one with two pairs of legs attached to it. Most have 40 legs or more.

Beautiful beetles

Beetles can be an amazing variety of shapes, sizes and colours, from tiny spotty red ladybirds, to huge beetles with horns and antlers.

Colourful critters

Colour in all these wonderfully patterned beetles, using the outline colours as a guide.

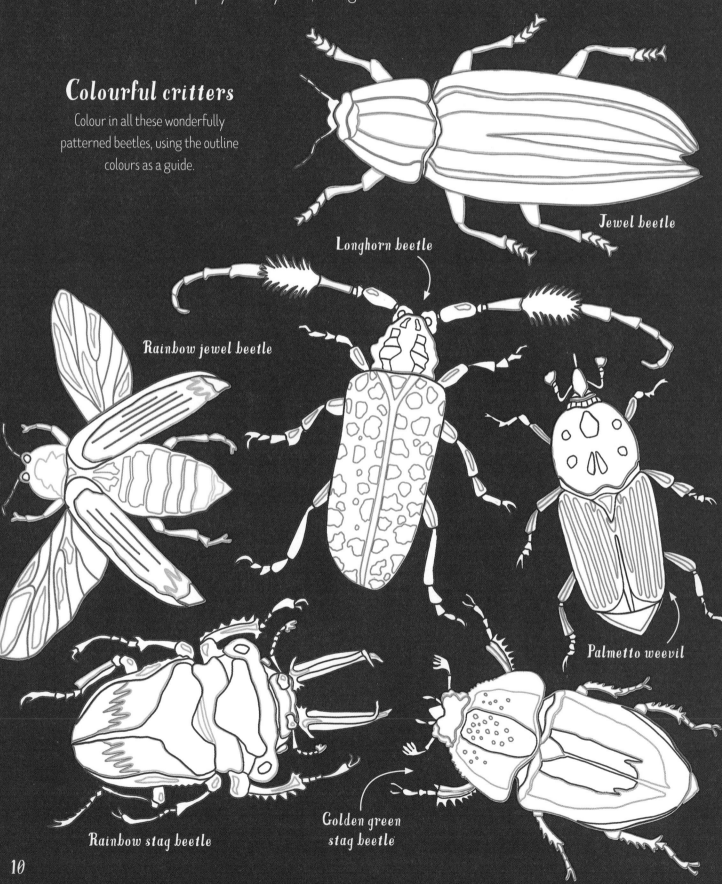

Jewel beetle

Longhorn beetle

Rainbow jewel beetle

Palmetto weevil

Rainbow stag beetle

Golden green stag beetle

Ladybird spots

Different types of ladybirds have different spots and patterns on their backs. Can you pick out three identical pairs among the ladybirds here?

Largest, smallest

Even though they're insects, some beetles can be huge. Read the descriptions of these big beetles, then number them from largest (1) to smallest (5).

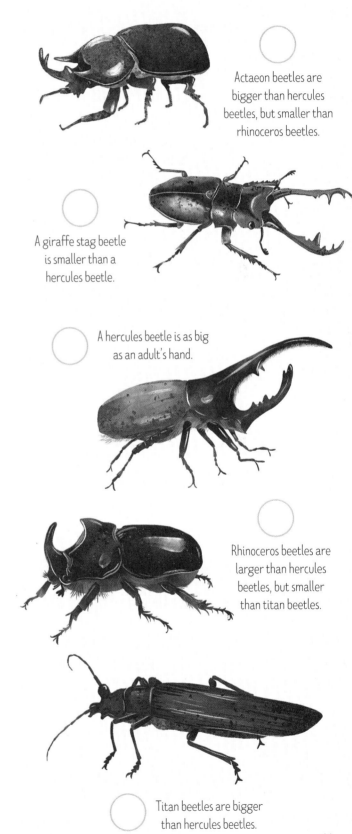

Actaeon beetles are bigger than hercules beetles, but smaller than rhinoceros beetles.

A giraffe stag beetle is smaller than a hercules beetle.

A hercules beetle is as big as an adult's hand.

Rhinoceros beetles are larger than hercules beetles, but smaller than titan beetles.

Titan beetles are bigger than hercules beetles.

11

In the pond

Down under the water, resting on top, hopping around or flying above,
all kinds of different creatures make ponds their home.

Pond dipping

Lots of animals have been scooped out of a pond. Can you identify the animal from its description, then write the correct number in the circle next to each one? Try to identify the animal that doesn't have a description, too.

1. Backswimmer
Swims upside-down underwater using its long back legs.

2. Whirligig beetle
Small, shiny round water beetle. Swims in circles on the surface of the water.

3. Water scorpion
Grabs food with its long pincers.

4. Pond skater
Has a light, thin body and long, thin legs. Balances on the surface.

5. Fairy shrimp
Tiny pond creature with 11 pairs of bristly legs, two tails and a curved body. Fairy shrimps live in groups.

6. ....

Walking on water
Over 1,000 different animals can 'walk', swim or balance on water. Basilisk lizards can sprint along the surface of water because they have extra flaps of skin on their toes which trap air. The air bubbles stop them from sinking.

Stickleback babies

A stickleback is a type of fish with spiky fins. Male sticklebacks have the job of looking after their babies when they hatch out.

Help this daddy stickleback catch his 10 little babies. Circle each one you find.

Dashing dragonflies

Dragonflies are dashing around hunting over a pond. Look at the first dragonfly below. Can you circle which other one looks exactly the same – A, B, C or D?

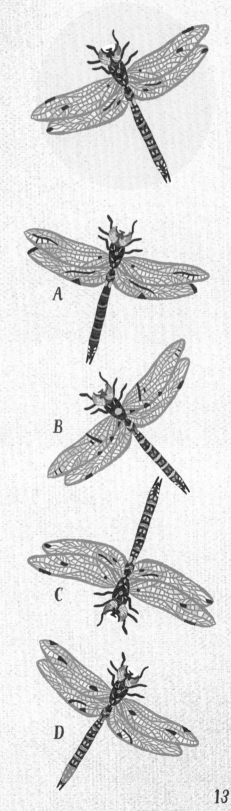

A

B

C

D

13

What is it?

Frogs, toads and newts go to ponds every spring to find partners and lay eggs.
These animals look similar, but there are ways to tell them apart. Read the descriptions
to work out whether it's a frog, toad or newt in each of the pictures.

Frog

Frogs have smooth, slimy skin,
narrow bodies and long legs.
Their noses are slightly pointy.
They jump to move around.

Toad

The skin of toads is rough and
dry with lots of spots and bumps.
Their bodies are wide with short
legs and round noses.

Newt

Newts have long, slimy bodies,
long, pointy tails and short legs.
Their faces are pointy too, with
small eyes. Some have frilly
crests on their backs.

Common ....

Green tree ....

American ....

Great crested ....

Natterjack ....

Frogs call to find partners.
Some can be VERY loud.
The loudest is the coqui tree frog
from Puerto Rico, which is as loud
as a lawn mower.

14

Growing frogs

Tiny tadpoles hatch from eggs called frogspawn, then gradually grow into frogs. This picture shows the different stages of a growing frog. Follow the instructions to finish drawing each stage, and then colour everything in.

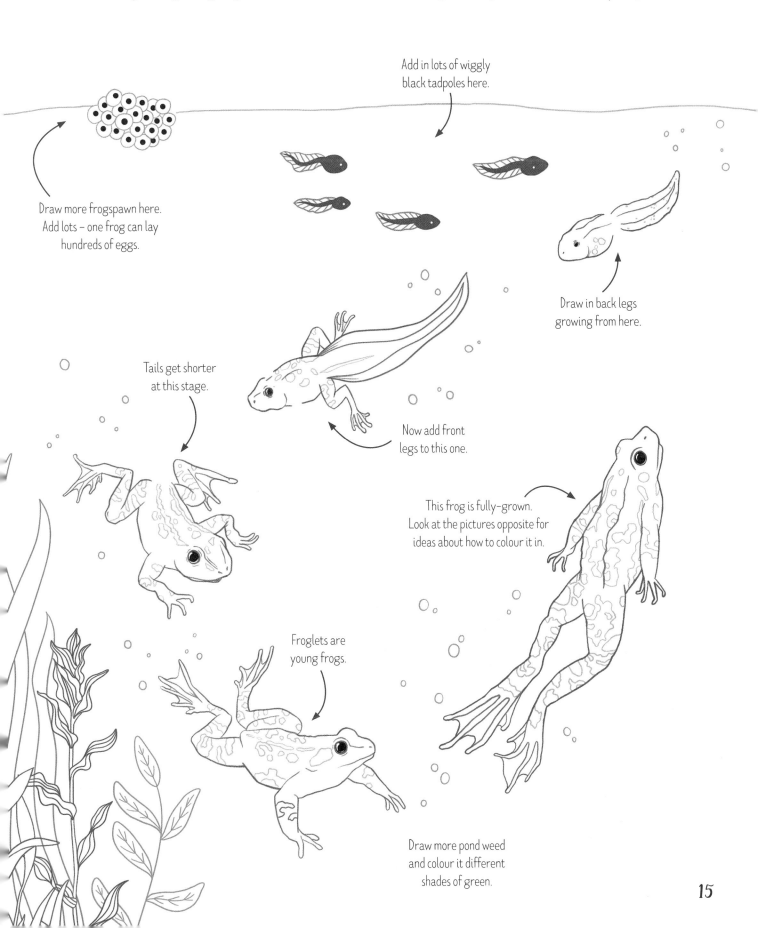

Add in lots of wiggly black tadpoles here.

Draw more frogspawn here. Add lots – one frog can lay hundreds of eggs.

Draw in back legs growing from here.

Tails get shorter at this stage.

Now add front legs to this one.

This frog is fully-grown. Look at the pictures opposite for ideas about how to colour it in.

Froglets are young frogs.

Draw more pond weed and colour it different shades of green.

It starts with a seed

Most plants grow from little seeds buried in the ground. Warmth, rain and sunshine makes the seeds swell and start to sprout.

How does it grow?

These pictures show different stages of a growing runner bean plant, but they're all mixed up. Can you add the numbers 1–8 in the circles to put them back in order?

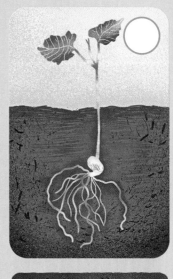

Seeds to plants

Try to match these seeds to the fruits, vegetables and flowers they grow into.

1. 2. 3. 4. 5. 6. 7.

Apple

Poppy

Sweet corn

Sunflower

Orange

Avocado

Pumpkin

How many grow?

Not all seeds that are planted will sprout and grow into plants,
so gardeners will often sow more seeds than they need.

Count the tomato seeds here. Half of them start to grow.
Of those that grow, a quarter will die before they're fully grown.
And only half of those that finish growing will produce tomatoes.
How many of the seeds will eventually grow tomatoes?

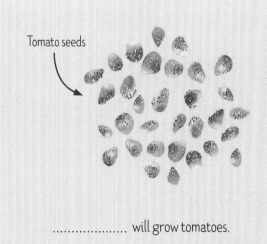

Tomato seeds

.... will grow tomatoes.

Busy border

A variety of different plants are growing in this busy border, with a mix of leaf shapes, colours, textures and flowers. Lots of bees are visiting the flowers.

Leafy bees

Wool carder bees scrape hairs from the leaves of fluffy lamb's ears, which they then use to line their nests. Can you find and circle all the wool carder bees carrying little bundles of fluff here?

Sea holly

Lamb's ear

Missing labels

Most of the plants in this border have labels for the gardener to remember what kinds of plants she is growing. But she's forgotten to write on three of them. Read the descriptions and fill in the blank labels with the missing plant names.

Chives
Plant with long, thin green leaves. Grows purple pompom flowers on stalks in the summer.

Fern
Each leaf uncurls into one leaf made up of lots of frilly smaller leaves.

Rosemary
Small, thin, spiky dark green leaves covering a whole stem.

Choisya

Hosta

Plant spotter
Can you work out which plants these leaves are from?

1.

2.

....

3.

4.

....

By the river

All kinds of creatures live in and around a wide, slow-flowing river running through the middle of a thick forest.

Beaver pool

Beavers build dams on rivers. The water behind floods into still pools, where they make nests, called lodges.

These little beaver pups have left their lodge to swim in the pool. Trace the line of river weed that will take them back home.

FINISH

START

River jumble

This picture is a jumble of different animals.
Can you spot the three that DON'T live in a river?

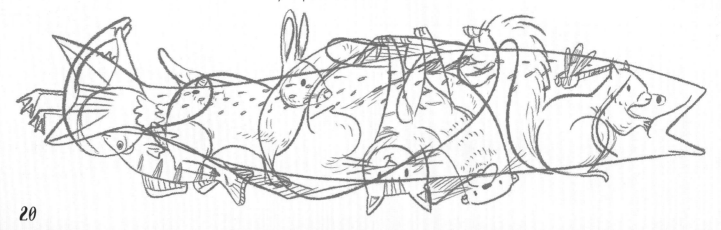

Hungry otters

Otters live in burrows in the banks of rivers. They dive
into the water to hunt for river creatures to eat.

Can you guess the missing letters to reveal the creatures
an otter would think of as a tasty meal?

1. WAT __ R
SN __ __ L

2. __ ATF __ SH

3. B __ L __
F __ OG

4. M __ YF __ Y
NYMPH

5. BR __ __ N
T __ __ UT

6. __ __ AYF __ S __

7. M __ __ SE __ __

Fish in hiding

Find and and circle the 10 small lake chubs hiding
among the stones, plants and other animals.

A chub looks like this:

Ants

Ants are always busy, scuttling around finding food, building nests or caring
for their young. Some dig long, winding tunnels underground or into
soft wood. Others make their homes inside nuts or leaves.

Ant food

Most ants collect plants and dead insects and carry them back
to their nests. Match the pieces the ants are carrying to the
food on the right. How many of each can you count?
Can you spot the ant carrying a young ant larva?

Grass seed ....

Hawk moth ....

European wasp ....

Plum ....

Which ant?

Fill in the missing letters to complete the names of each type of ant.
The descriptions give you clues about what the ants are called.

1. Makes nests in hollow nuts.

_ CO _ N ANT

2. When this ant stings, it
feels hot and burning.

F _ R _ ANT

3. Digs holes into wood
and lays eggs inside.

C _ RP _ NT _ R ANT

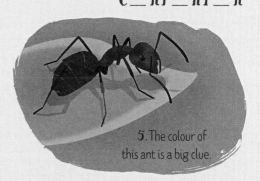

4. Chops plants into pieces to make food.

L _ _ F C _ TT _ R ANT

5. The colour of
this ant is a big clue.

COMMON B _ _ _ K ANT

Wood ant maze

Wood ants dig nests into rotting tree stumps. They cover them with a thick layer of pine needles to keep out the rain and cold. Worker ants collect pine needles and bring food back to the nest, too.

Find a way back to the nest for both ants in this maze. They can't cross other lines of ants, and they must avoid the beetles and spiders that want to eat them.

Ant with food

Ant with pine needle

NEST

Bird watching

Keen bird watchers travel far and wide to spot their favourite birds. They study birds' markings, how they behave and fly, and even what birds do when they're getting ready for bed.

Flying birds

It's possible to spot some birds by the shapes they make when they're flying.
Can you match these birds to their flying silhouettes?

Long-tailed tit   **Lapwing**   **Red kite**   **Whooper swan**

Different jays

Some birds from the same family can look very similar, *but* they're not exactly the same. Look at the blue jay on the far left first. Then circle two differences on *each* of the other jays on the branch.

Going home to roost

As the sun goes down, some birds will fly around together in groups before they settle down to sleep, or roost. Groups are easy to tell apart because they make particular shapes in the sky.

In this evening sky, a few of the birds in each flock have been drawn already. Read the descriptions and then draw in the rest to complete the shapes.

Geese fly in a side-on v-shape. Complete the 'v' here by adding more geese.

Crows fly close to trees in big, messy groups. Draw more flying in to roost.

Small groups of ducks dash across the sky in a line. Add three more flying here.

Starling flocks make strange shapes, a bit like huge, swirling clouds. Can you fill in the gap?

Woodland birds

Unjumble the letters to name the woodland birds.
Can you spot each one in the surrounding trees?
Write the matching numbers in the circles next to the birds.

1. WATNY WOL

_ _ _ _ _   _ _ _

Reddish-brown bird of prey that nests in
holes in trees. Makes a 'twit-twoo' call.

2. OOWD IPOEGN

_ _ _ _ _   _ _ _ _ _ _

Large grey bird with a white patch on its neck and
bright yellow rings around its eyes.

3. LUEB TTI

_ _ _ _   _ _ _

Small with a bright blue head, wings and tail.
From a family of birds called 'tits'.

4. TEER PRECEER

_ _ _ _ _   _ _ _ _ _ _ _

Creeps up trees, looking for grubs in the bark.
Brown with a white tummy.

5. NOLG-DIALTE ITT

_ _ _ _ _ - _ _ _ _ _ _ _   _ _ _

Small bird from the tit family, with pink markings and tail longer than its body. Lives in groups.

6. EERGN KWDOPOECRE

_ _ _ _ _   _ _ _ _ _ _ _ _ _ _

Large and green with a long, sharp beak to peck holes in
trees while searching for food.

Fabulous feathers

The easiest way to identify a bird is by the colour and markings on its feathers. Sometimes it's possible to see incredible colour variation on just one feather. Using the completed feathers as a guide, colour in the markings on these feathers.

Blue jay   Kingfisher   Pheasant   Wood duck

Nature at night

While people are tucked up in bed at night, lots of
animals are awake and busy.

Glowing fireflies

Fireflies are beetles that come out at night. They can make
their own light, which they flash on and off to find partners.
There are 18 glowing fireflies on these pages.
See if you can spot them.

Animal eyes

There are lots of animals hidden in the darkness here.
Some of them have glowing eyes, which reflect light
and shine different colours. Can you find them all?

Fox: RED   Owl: YELLOW
Frog: GREEN   Raccoon: BLUE

Many moths

Moths wake up as the sun goes down and spend the night fluttering around looking for food and partners.

They're attracted to light, so will often fly around streetlights. How many of each of these moths can you spot flying in the picture? And which one isn't there at all?

The missing moth is: ....

Garden tiger moth ....

Luna moth ....

Spotted hawkmoth ....

Sphinx moth ....

Imperial moth ....

Regal moth ....

Night animals

Can you guess which two of these animals aren't awake at night?

Carrion crow

Garden snail

Badger

Common toad

House mouse

Adder

Common pipistrelle bat

Snakes and lizards

Snakes and lizards have smooth, scaly skin, beady eyes and flicking tongues.
They slither or scamper around the undergrowth hunting animals to eat.

Hidden lizards

Many lizards have patterns on their skin so they blend in with their surroundings. This makes other animals less likely to spot and eat them. Can you spot 20 lizards hidden among these rocks?

Shedding skin

When snakes and lizards grow, their skin doesn't. Instead, it gets tighter and tighter, until it finally splits and falls off. Underneath, is brand new baggy skin for them to grow into.

Lizard or snake?

Usually, snakes and lizards are easy to tell apart – lizards have legs and snakes don't. But some lizards have very small legs hidden under their bodies, or even no legs at all.

Can you guess which of the animals here are snakes, and which are lizards? Read the 'Reptile hints' to help you.

Reptile hints

Lizards have visible ears – little holes on the sides of their heads.

Snakes have thin, forked tongues. Lizards' tongues are thicker and less forked.

Lizards have visible eyelids but snakes don't.

Skinks are lizards with long bodies and tiny legs.

A horned viper is a

....

Burton's ....

Garter ....

Scarlet king ....

Burrowing ....

Glass ....

How long?

Snakes and lizards can't warm up on their own, so they need to lie, or bask, in the sun every day to soak up warmth before they go out to hunt. Smaller snakes and lizards warm up more quickly than larger ones. In hot deserts, they bask in the early morning sun, or at night, on rocks still warm from the day's heat.

Can you work out the length of time these two lizards and snake need to bask – A, B or C?

A 7 – 10am

B 2 – 3.30am

C 9 – 9.45am

Gila monster

Size: 60cm (2ft) long
Habitat: deserts, southwestern USA

European green lizard

Size: 40cm (16in)
Habitat: woodland and hedgerows, central Europe

Corn snake

Size: 90cm (3ft)
Habitat: overgrown fields, southeastern USA

Lots of leaves

Leaves have a big job. They take in sunlight, air and water, and turn it into food to help the plant grow big and healthy.

Leafy shapes

From big, flat round leaves to tiny ones covered in scales, leaves can be lots of different shapes, colours and textures. Finish off the leaves on this page, by adding ones or completing patterns or veins. Then colour everything in.

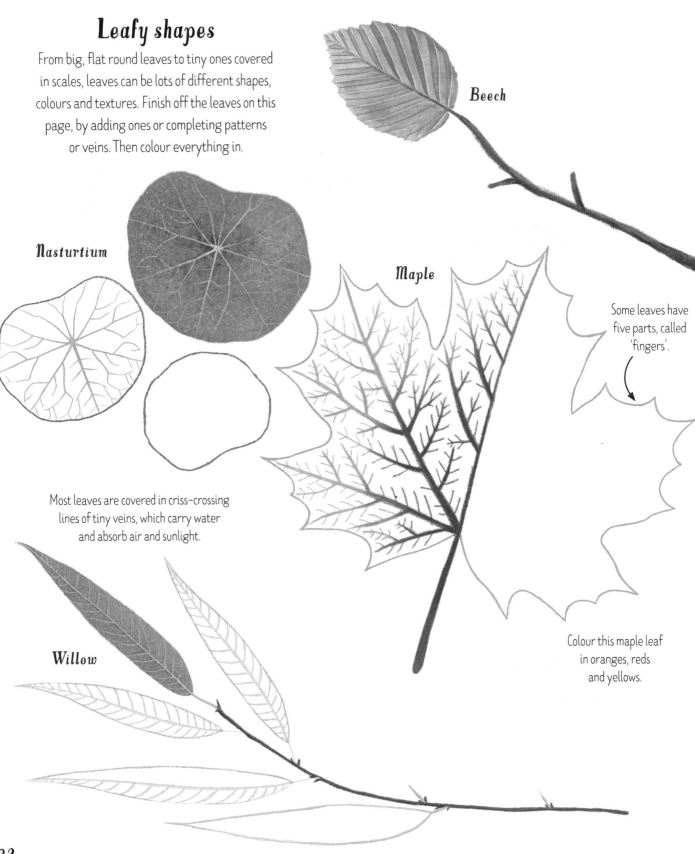

Beech

Nasturtium

Maple

Some leaves have five parts, called 'fingers'.

Most leaves are covered in criss-crossing lines of tiny veins, which carry water and absorb air and sunlight.

Willow

Colour this maple leaf in oranges, reds and yellows.

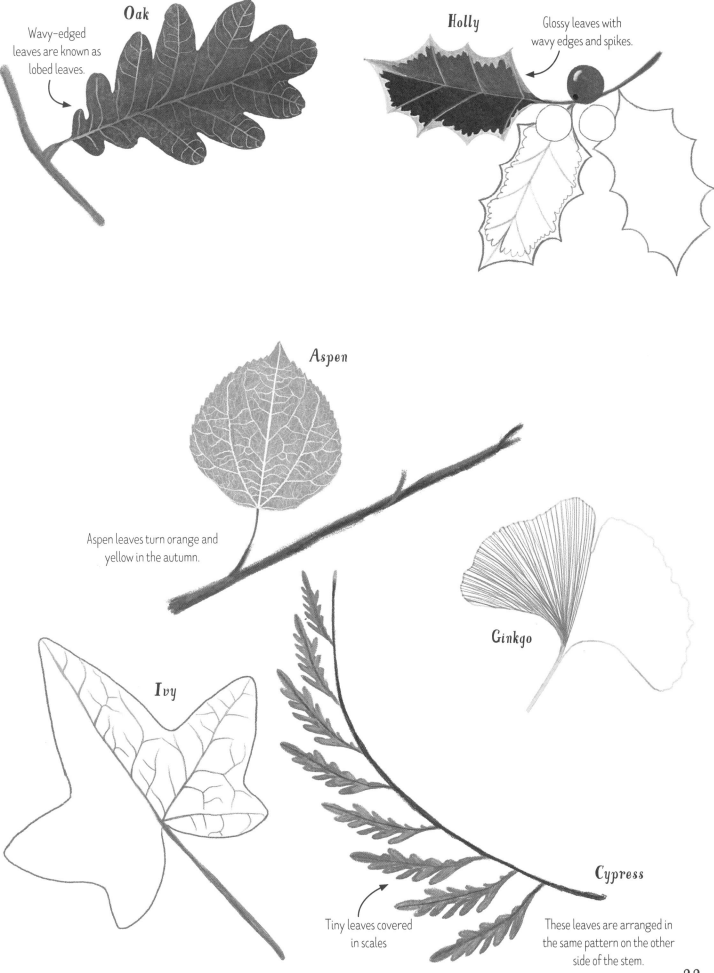

Oak

Wavy-edged leaves are known as lobed leaves.

Holly

Glossy leaves with wavy edges and spikes.

Aspen

Aspen leaves turn orange and yellow in the autumn.

Ginkgo

Ivy

Cypress

Tiny leaves covered in scales

These leaves are arranged in the same pattern on the other side of the stem.

In the woods

Dark and mysterious woods are full of tall trees, tangled shrubs
and vines, and frondy ferns and flowers growing on the shady ground. All kinds
of creatures hide among the branches and in the undergrowth, too.

Story telling

Woods have been the setting
for many tales, myths and legends.
Choose one of the story starters below
and write a short story in the space.

*There was a light up ahead.
Was it a cabin? Or something else?*

*It was the biggest tree they'd
ever seen! But the more they
studied it, the stranger it seemed...*

*Two paths stretched before her
into the dark, dense woods.
She had to pick one...*

How old?

Trees grow by adding one layer to their
trunks every year. When a tree is cut
down, you can see all the layers
as rings. These trees were cut
down on 1st December, 2017. Can you work out
the year they each first started to grow?

1. ....   2. ....   3. ....

Woodland quiz

Test your knowledge of trees, woodland plants and animals in this quiz.

1. Which of these plants would you NOT find growing in a woodland?

a) Liverwort   d) Barrel cactus

b) Wild garlic   e) Foxglove

c) Honeysuckle   f) Moss

2. Match the names of these woodland trees to their nuts, seeds or fruit:

1. Oak   2. Maple   3. Horse chestnut   4. Crab apple

a)

b)

c)

d)

3. The tallest tree in the world is a California redwood called 'Hyperion'. At 115m (379ft), this is almost as tall as:

a) A double-decker bus

b) The Great Pyramid in Egypt

c) A giraffe

4. True or false? More animals live in woods and forests than anywhere else on earth.

TRUE / FALSE

5. Only TWO of these animals live in woods. Which ones?

a) Seagull

b) Manatee

c) American goldfinch

d) Camel spider

e) Wildcat

f) Polar bear

6. Mushrooms grow on the damp, shady woodland floor. Some have pretty strange names. Which one of these is NOT a mushroom?

a) Witch's butter   d) Budgie fungus

b) Shaggy ink cap   e) Giant puffball

c) Chicken of the woods f) Hedgehog mushroom

On the seashore

Seashores are where the sea meets land – vast, sandy beaches,
steep, rocky cliffs or stony ground covered in shallow pools.

Seashore hunt

All kinds of shells, sea creatures, plants and pebbles
wash up on beaches. Can you spot and circle these
things on this seashore?

One abalone shell

Eight periwinkle shells

Four scallop shells

One heart urchin shell

Two pieces of driftwood

Bladderwrack seaweed

Three bones of a cuttlefish

Five crab claws

Tide puzzle

When the sea comes further up the beach, or goes further out, it's called a tide. When the sea is furthest out is low tide, and furthest up is called high tide. A high and low tide always has roughly 12 hours between them.

Friends are planning a trip to the beach. They want to arrive around 9am, leave no later than 5pm, and don't want to risk being there at high tide. Study the tide table and work out which day they should go to the beach.

Best day to visit: ....

Tide Table

Key: ▲ High tide   ▽ Low tide

7th July	14th July	1st August	12th August
▲ 3.05am	▲ 6.09am	▲ 9.12am	▲ 10.42am
▽ 9.10am	▽ 11.20am	▽ 1.01pm	▽ 2.33pm
▲ 3.15pm	▲ 6.01pm	▲ 8.49pm	▲ 10.03pm
▽ 9.06pm	▽ 11.11pm	▽ 1.24am	▽ 2.54am

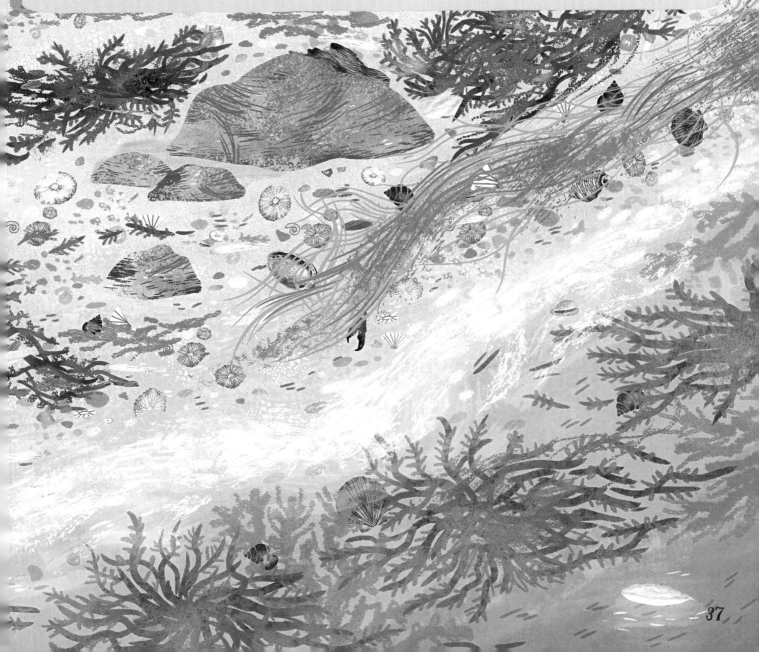

Rock pool word search

Rock pools are small pools on the seashore where water collects between rocks. Many sea creatures live in the pools. Which one of these creatures *isn't* hidden in the word search?

Shore crab
A small crab that hunts in rock pools.

Starfish
A sea creature with five 'arms'.

Shrimp
A small sea creature with a shell, four pairs of legs and long feelers.

Anemone
Uses its stinging tentacles to catch other animals.

Limpet
Sea snail with a very hard shell.

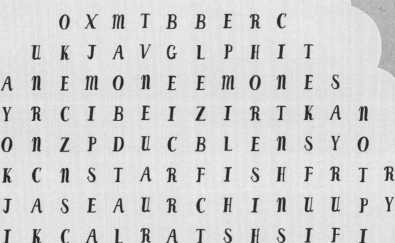

```
Q B I A P T L
O X M T B B E R C
U K J A V G L P H I T
A N E M O N E E M O N E S
D Y R C I B E I Z I R T K A N
M O N Z P D U C B L E N S Y O
H A K C N S T A R F I S H F R T R
M E J A S E A U R C H I N U U P Y
P I K C A L R A T S H S I F I
V M K C A B E L K C I T S
B T A I R S S E Y
O B E N N Y S
P M I R H S E
```

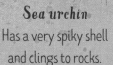

Sea urchin
Has a very spiky shell and clings to rocks.

Stickleback
Fish with spiny fins on its back.

Blenny
Small fish with big eyes. Lives at the bottom of rock pools.

Before and after

The sea washes different creatures in and out of rock pools, as the tide comes up
and down the beach each day. Look at this rock pool, before and after the
tide has come. Can you circle 15 differences in the 'After' picture?

Before

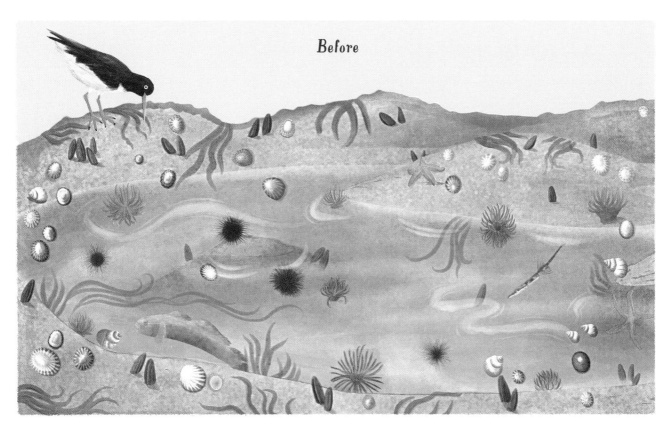

After

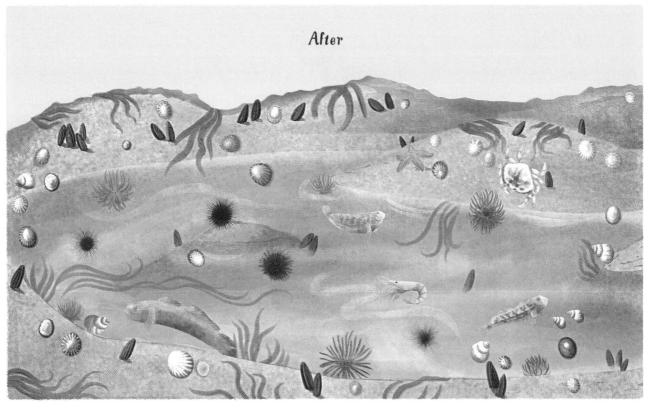

Fluttering butterflies

Butterflies flutter from flower to flower in the summer, stopping to feed or rest in the warm sun. The colourful patterns on their wings shimmer when they catch the light.

Colour by numbers

Following the numbers in the key, colour in the patterns on the butterfly wings.

Peacock

Orange tip

Small tortoiseshell

Swallowtail

Red admiral

Caterpillar to butterfly

Butterflies begin their lives as tiny caterpillars. Then they spend their days eating and growing bigger, until they turn into butterflies. These sketches and notes follow the life cycle of a monarch caterpillar, but they've all been mixed up. Write the numbers 1–9 in the circles to put them back in order.

Butterfly crawls out. Wings are wet and crumpled.

Skin splits and there's harder skin underneath. This is called a pupa.

Caterpillar grows bigger and skin splits again. Even more colourful.

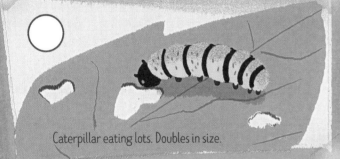

Caterpillar eating lots. Doubles in size.

Wings dry. Butterfly flies away.

Skin splits and bigger caterpillar crawls out. More colourful patterns.

Biggest ever! Crawls under leaf and hangs upside down.

Ten days later, pupa turns see-through.

Caterpillar hatches out of egg. Eats the egg and leaf straight away.

Autumn

In autumn, the weather begins to cool, and tree branches become heavy with fruit, nuts and seeds. Leaves gradually turn from green to red, orange and yellow, before dropping to the ground.

Changing scene

Trees and other plants can change very quickly. Animals hurry around collecting food to store for the winter, and gobbling up fallen fruit. Others hide away, or fly off in search of warmer weather. Look at these two pictures of the same scene a few weeks apart. Can you spot 18 things that have changed in the second picture?

Falling leaves

A gust of wind has sent lots of leaves fluttering off their branches to the woodland floor. Draw different leaves here, then colour them shades of red, orange, yellow and brown. You could look on pages 32-33 for ideas.

1. Sycamore

7. Elder

6. Horse chestnut

Nuts, fruits and seeds

Trees, vines and bushes grow seeds in the autumn.
Some seeds have tough cases. Others grow inside fleshy fruits.

Look at the fruit, nuts and seeds below, and match them up to the tree
that grew them. Clue: looking at the names and leaves will help you.

Cone

Helicopter seeds

Rosehips

Acorns

2. Oak

Elderberries

Sloes

3. Dog rose

Conkers

5. Pine

4. Blackthorn

Autumn words

What words or feelings do you associate with autumn? They could be to do with animals, plants or the weather, or the way things change during the season. Write down your ideas...

Oranges and reds

Falling leaves

Misty

...then, you could write a short story or poem using some of these words.

At the nature reserve

A nature reserve is an important area for wildlife. Lots of animals make their nests or find food in reserves, and people can visit to learn more about them.

Which reserve?

Alex, Evie, Saba and Oliver are keen bird watchers. Read about them, then look at the leaflets for different nature reserves. Match each bird watcher with the reserve you think they'd most like to visit.

Evie
I love getting away from it all to spot birds, especially where it's open and a bit wild. I'm mainly interested in birds of prey.

Alex
My favourite times of year are spring and autumn. I love birds of prey and spotting birds in unexpected places.

Oliver
I think autumn is by far the best time to get out and about. I'd ideally like to see woodpeckers, treecreepers, long-tailed tits and other woodland birds.

Saba
I like all kinds of birds, but ones that live in or around water are my favourites – kingfishers in woodland rivers and waterfowl near the sea.

Bare Hill
Wonderful wild scrubland with grouse, wheatear, and birds of prey sighted regularly. May be closed in autumn and winter due to snow blocking mountain roads.

Golden Woods
The best time to visit the Golden Woods is during autumn, when the leaves turn reds, yellows and oranges. Look out for lots of woodland birds, especially around the beautiful river.

Big City Reserve
Find out just how much you can spot in the middle of a city. You might be surprised to see peregrine falcons, sparrowhawks and green woodpeckers only minutes away from the city centre.

Little Bay Estuary
Take a walk by the wide river as it winds its way through marshland to the sea. Watch lots of river and marsh birds feeding in late autumn, including black-headed gulls and oystercatchers.

Visiting the reserve

Three friends are visiting Sea View Reserve for the day. They want to see all the animals in the reserve, visit a café, and go to the gift shop, too. But they don't want to visit the museum. Can you draw a route around this map of the reserve so they get to see what they want, without seeing anything twice?

EXIT

ENTRANCE

Gift shop

Seal beach
Common seals

Sheep field

Butterfly meadow

Seaview café

Scrubland
Hares and skylarks

Mudflats
for wading birds such as avocets and spoonbills

Saltmarsh
for greylag geese and whooper swans

Reserve museum

Viewing area
Sea otters and gulls

47

On the move

Some animals migrate – they fly, swim or trek long distances in search of food or warmer weather.

Journey map

This map shows the routes of Mexican free-tailed bats and monarch butterflies as they go on their journeys. They stop off along the way to rest.

Looking at the map and the table below, can you calculate the total number of days it takes the butterflies to go from Escanaba to Cerro Pelon, and the bats from Michoacan to Yolo Bypass Bridge? Write the answer in the blank column in the table.

Yolo Bypass Bridge

Escanaba

CANADA

Magazine Mountain
Stop off five days

Maviri
Stop off three days

MEXICO

USA

Brownsville
Stop off two days

PACIFIC OCEAN

CARRIBBEAN SEA

Michoacan

Cerro Pelon

Animal	Leaving from	Arriving in	Number of days	Total days to reach destination
Mexican free-tailed bat	Michoacan	Maviri	8	
	Maviri	Yolo Bypass Bridge	12	
Monarch butterfly	Escanaba	Magazine Mountain	12	
	Magazine Mountain	Brownsville	11	
	Brownsville	Cerro Pelon	8	

Animal journeys

Here are some animals that go on migration, where they travel from and to, and the distance they travel. Can you match up the distances with the correct animals?

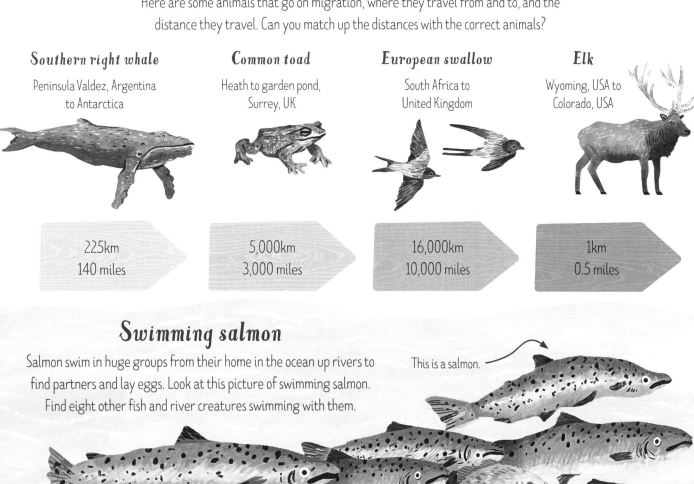

Southern right whale
Peninsula Valdez, Argentina to Antarctica

Common toad
Heath to garden pond, Surrey, UK

European swallow
South Africa to United Kingdom

Elk
Wyoming, USA to Colorado, USA

225km
140 miles

5,000km
3,000 miles

16,000km
10,000 miles

1km
0.5 miles

Swimming salmon

Salmon swim in huge groups from their home in the ocean up rivers to find partners and lay eggs. Look at this picture of swimming salmon. Find eight other fish and river creatures swimming with them.

This is a salmon.

Amazing mushrooms

Mushrooms pop up from damp ground, tree trunks and soggy, rotting wood.
They're the fruit of big, underground living things, called fungi.

Fungus quiz

Test how good your knowledge of mushrooms is in this fiendish fungus quiz.

1. Many mushrooms are poisonous, and have names or bright colouring that warn people and animals not to eat them. Can you guess which one of these mushrooms is safe to eat?

a) Death cap

b) Penny bun

c) Destroying angels

d) Deadly dapperling

e) Fly agaric

2. The largest living thing in the world is a:

a) Honey fungus
b) Blue whale
c) Giant redwood tree

3. True or false? Mushrooms need sunlight to grow.

TRUE / FALSE

4. Match these mushrooms to their names:

1.   2.   3.

a) Stag's horn   b) Witches' butter   c) Jelly ear

Super seeds

Mushrooms produce tiny, tiny seeds, called spores, which they spread in different ways.

Giant puffball mushrooms explode, sending a big puff of seeds high into the air.

5. True or false? Over 70 different types of mushroom glow in the dark.

TRUE / FALSE

Mushroom forest

Mushrooms can be an incredible variety of shapes and colours. Fill this forest with fungi, using the examples in the 'Tree trunks' and 'Forest floor and fallen trees' boxes.

Tree trunks

Turkey tail

Chicken of the woods

Forest floor and fallen trees

Blusher

Chantarelle

Morel

Shaggy ink cap

Amethyst deceiver

Animal homes

High up in a tall tree or deep under the ground, animals make their homes in all kinds of different places.

Missing vowels

The vowels (A, E, I, O and U) have been taken out of the names of different animal homes on this page. Can you fill in the gaps?

B _ T'S R _ _ ST

B _ RD'S N _ ST

R _ BB _ T W _ RR _ N

B _ _ H _ V _

_ NTH _ LL

F _ SH P _ ND

SP _ D _ R'S W _ B

F _ X'S D _ N

Which home?

Can you match these animals to their homes?

Eagle   Squirrel   Beaver   Bear

Den   Lodge   Drey   Eyrie

Burrow maze

Prairie dogs live in huge underground burrows with lots of chambers. Draw a route from the entrance to the exit, visiting the toilet chamber, nursery and three food stores, but avoiding dead-ends and dangerous prairie rattlesnakes.

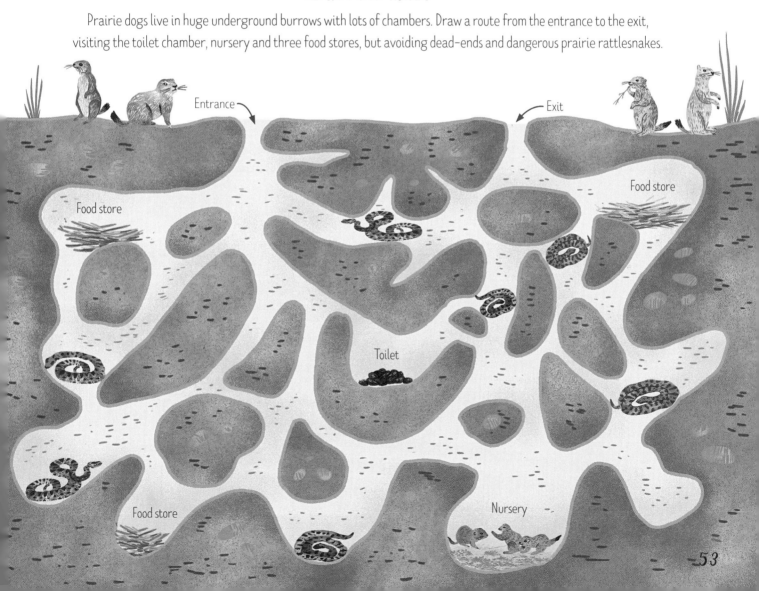

Entrance   Exit

Food store   Food store

Toilet

Food store   Nursery

53

Cloudy skies

There lots of different types of clouds – and you can even predict the weather by studying them.

Cirrocumulus – tiny, fluffy white clouds. In winter, this means fair but cold weather on the way. In summer, it could mean an approaching storm.

Cumulonimbus – tall, dark clouds. There will probably be a storm with thunder and lightning.

Cumulus – big, white, fluffy clouds. Usually means fair weather, unless they're getting bigger. Then there might be a storm later in the day.

Stratus – thick blanket of cloud low down in the sky. Might mean drizzle or snow.

Be a weather forecaster

Here are some cloudy skies on different mornings, in different places, and at different times of year. Look at the clouds and descriptions, then write down which type of cloud is in each sky. Can you predict what the weather will be like later each day, too?

1.

Cloud type:
....

Weather prediction:
....
....
....

2.

Cloud type:
....

Weather prediction:
....
....
....

3.

Cloud type:
....

Weather prediction:
....
....
....

4.

7am

9am

Cloud type:
....

Weather prediction:
....
....
....

Cloud diary

Look out your window and draw the clouds in the spaces on this page. If you can, look in the morning, then again in the afternoon. Do the clouds change throughout the day? You could try predicting the weather, using the tips opposite.

Morning clouds:

While looking up at the sky, never ever look directly at the Sun. It could seriously damage your eyes.

Are any clouds interesting shapes?

If you see any birds flying, you could draw these in, too.

Prediction: ....
....

Afternoon clouds:

Is there anything else you notice in the sky? Long, thin lines of cloud are contrails, made by planes.

Winter

In the depths of a very cold winter, snow covers the ground and frost glimmers on bare branches. Hungry creatures hunt around for food.

Winter sky

The Sun sets early and rises late in winter. As the sky grows dark on a cold night, thousands of stars appear.

Some groups of stars look like patterns in the sky, known as constellations. Try to join the lines between these stars to make the constellations in the box.

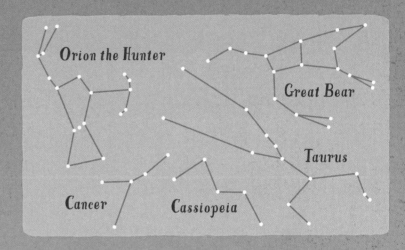

Orion the Hunter

Great Bear

Taurus

Cancer

Cassiopeia

Bark match

After trees lose their leaves in winter, it's easier to see the colour and texture of the bark.

Look at the tree trunks here, then match them to the close-ups of the different barks below.

A.

B.

C.

D.

E.

○ Plane

○ Sweet chestnut

○ Birch

○ Oak

○ Sequoia

Footprints in the snow

Lots of different animals have walked over a patch of snow, leaving a jumble of footprints. Looking at the animal prints in the box, circle each footprint as you spot it, then work out which animal hasn't been there.

Animal prints

Weasel

Rat

Magpie

Wild boar

Squirrel

Badger

Otter

Snowflakes

Snow is made of tiny flakes, crystals of ice that form into intricate, beautiful shapes called snowflakes. They can look similar, but no two snowflakes are exactly the same.

Fill these pages with lots of falling snowflakes.
Add decoration to the lines drawn here,
or create your own from scratch.

Some snowflakes are
shaped like needles,
columns or arrowheads.

Food for everyone

Plant-eaters, meat-eaters, or a bit of both-eaters, different animals hunt for different types of food.

Storing food

Some animals collect food in autumn and hide it so they'll have enough to eat through winter.

A jay has collected acorns, and buried them in different places. But he will forget where he's buried half of them, and a quarter of the remaining ones will be dug up by other animals. How many will he find to eat in total?

................acorns

9 acorns

2 acorns

3 acorns

4 acorns

6 acorns

Which food?

Can you match each animal to the food it eats? Here are some clues to help you:

Animals that eat other animals have long, pointy front teeth or sharp, hooked beaks and claws.

Some birds eat both insects and plants.

Most owls only catch food they can carry.

Rabbits only eat plants.

Grey squirrels eat a range of nuts and fruits.

1. Sparrow

2. Wolf

3. Rabbit

4. Grey squirrel

5. Little owl

A. Grass

B. Caterpillars and seeds

C. Deer

D. Mouse

E. Hazelnuts and rowan berries

Picking over pellets

Birds of prey, seagulls and some other birds swallow their food whole, and bring up anything that they can't digest (such as bones, fur and seeds) in pellets.

Using the pictures on the right, can you work out what each bird has eaten by looking at their pellets? Sometimes you'll see pieces of food, rather than the whole thing.

Crow

....
....
....
....

Short-eared owl

....
....

Herring gull

....
....
....

Blackbird

....
....
....

Buzzard

....
....
....
....

Vole (skull)

Wheat (seeds)

Clam (shell)

Mouse (fur)

Ground beetle (wing cases)

Damson (seeds)

Fish (bones)

Millipede (tough case)

Dry grass (stalks)

At sea

In and around a rough sea, birds dive into the water to catch fish, and seals laze on the shore.
Unusual creatures and plants make their homes just under the rolling waves, too.

Lounging seals

These seals have crowded onto a beach to bring
up their young pups. Can you count how many
adults there are? Then find the seal pups.
Clue: they're a different colour than the adults.

.... adults and .... pups

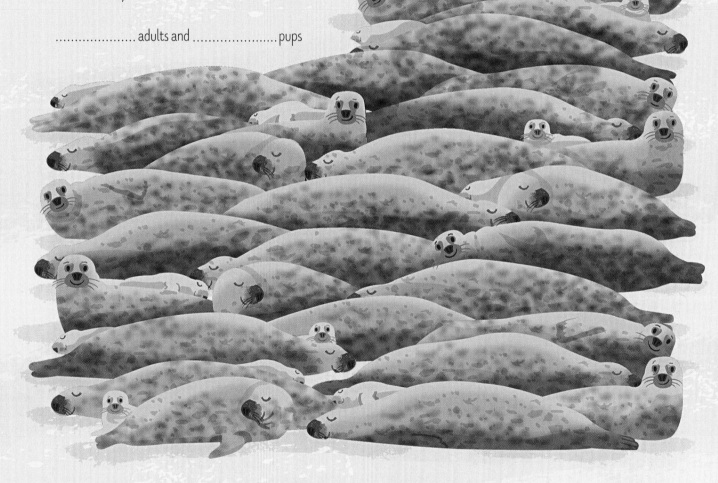

Underwater hunters

Hungry seals dive into the sea to hunt
for fish and other sea creatures.
They can hold their breaths for up
to an impressive 30 minutes. Some even
go to sleep underwater.

zzz

Sea forecast

The weather at sea can change quickly. Anyone planning a sailing trip should check the weather forecast very carefully before setting off.

Two friends are planning a trip by boat to visit a Scottish island known for its wildlife. They want to arrive mid-morning, then spend four to five hours exploring before coming home. Study the weather forecast for the island for three different days below. Which day would be the best to visit?

6th May

- 7am Showers, light winds, warm
- 10am Sunny intervals, breezy, warm
- 1pm Drizzle, strong winds, cool
- 4pm Heavy rain, strong winds, cool

11th May

- 7am Sunny, light winds, warm
- 10am Drizzle, light winds, warm
- 1pm Rain showers, light winds, warm
- 4pm Rain showers, light winds, cool

15th May

- 7am Sunny, light winds, warm
- 10am Thundery showers, strong winds, cool
- 1pm Rain showers, strong winds, cool
- 4pm Heavy rain, breezy, cool

Best day to visit: ....

Hungry puffins

Puffins are sea birds with bright, striped beaks. They catch fish to feed to their chicks who wait in burrows on the shore.

Help this mother puffin get a beakful of fish back to her chick, avoiding the greedy gulls and other puffins who want to steal her catch.

MOTHER PUFFIN

CHICK

Sea creature spiral

Find and circle the names of 15 sea creatures hidden in the whirpool of words.

The spiral of letters reads:

SANDSEASEALWAVESPARROTFISHBOATCLOWNFISHFISHERMANSEASLUGSTORMDOLPHINOCTOPUSPORTKNOTSHULLSHELLEHERMITCRABCONCHJIBBOARDWALKJELLYFISHLIFEBOATSEATURTLECAPTAINCUTTLEFISHSEAKALESANDEELWHEELHOUSESQUIDGIANTCLAMPORTICULISNAUTILUSDECK

Turtle generations

Sea turtles crawl onto beaches to lay their eggs. Tiny baby turtles hatch out, then make their way back to the sea to grow up and eventually have babies of their own.

One sea turtle lays eight eggs. When they hatch out, half are female. Those females go on to lay six eggs each.

If all the eggs hatch, how many turtle babies will there be?

....

Coral reefs

Coral reefs are huge, underwater structures, made up of strange plant-like animals called corals.
They're also home to an incredible quarter of all sea creatures, who find shelter and plenty of food there.
Using the clues, match the locations of these different reefs to the highlighted areas on the map.

1. Great Barrier Reef
2. Minami-Tori-shima Reef

3. Belize Barrier Reef
4. Sula Reef

5. Bar Reef
6. Florida Barrier Reef

Clues

The Bar Reef is further south than
the Minami-Tori-shima Reef.

The Great Barrier Reef is furthest south.

The Belize Barrier Reef is further west
than the Sula reef.

The Florida Barrier Reef is north of the
Belize Barrier Reef and west of the Sula Reef.

The Sula Reef is further north than the others.

Match the corals

Corals can be many different shapes, and they're often named
after the way they look. Can you match these names to the corals,
and other sea creatures, in this scene?

1. Fan coral
2. Pillar coral
3. Brain coral

4. Staghorn coral
5. Starfish
6. Giant clam

65

Spiders

Spiders weave sticky webs to catch animals to eat, or chase after them using their eight scuttling legs. They have fangs for injecting venom, or poison, to stun their prey.

1.

Magic markings

Some spiders have distinctive markings on their bodies and legs. Can you match the zoomed in details of the spider markings to the spiders?

Jumping spider ◯

Red-knee tarantula

Wasp spider ◯

Black widow ◯

Garden spider ◯

2.

3.

4.

5.

Spider true or false?

One of these spider facts is false. Can you guess which one?

Water spiders live underwater in round, air-filled webs.

Trapdoor spiders live in underground burrows. They make a little 'door' that they open to pounce on passing bugs.

Air spiders float up high in the sky using wings made from webs.

Sand spiders bury themselves in sand to hide from their prey.

Wonderful webs

Spiders make their webs from sticky silk that comes from their bodies.
Webs can be different shapes – neat spirals between tree branches, messy,
tangled lines in a clump, or thick tunnels where the spider hides deep inside.

Follow the silk strands coming from each spider to find out which web
they've woven. Which spider hasn't made a web?

C

3.

D

**Hammock-
weaver**

**Green-fanged
spider**

2.

B

Wolf spider

1.

**Marbled orb
weaver**

A

False widow

E

4.

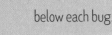

Spider food

After you've matched up the spiders to their
webs, can you identify what they've caught?
Write the correct letter in the circle
below each bug.

Oak tree moth　　**Cockroach**　　**House fly**　　**Sawfly**　　**Green bottle fly**

( )　　　( )　　　( )　　　( )　　　( )

Springtime

Spring has finally arrived. Flowers, buds and leaves are just beginning to grow, and birds, bugs and other animals are busy building nests.

Baby animals

Lots of animals have babies in springtime, and many have different names from their parents. Can you name the baby animals here? The first letter of each is given to help you.

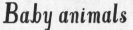

1. C _ _ _ _ _

3. P _ _ _

2. F _ _ _ _

4. C _ _

5. L _ _ _ _

6. F _ _ _ _

True or false?

Decide whether these statements are true or false.

1. The first spring flowers to grow are poppies.

TRUE / FALSE

2. On the first day of spring, called the equinox, both day and night last for exactly 12 hours.

TRUE / FALSE

3. Baby squirrels are called kittens.

TRUE / FALSE

4. Spring is at the same time of year all over the world.

TRUE / FALSE

5. Birds sing much more in spring, as they try to attract mates.

TRUE / FALSE

6. All trees grow blossom in spring.

TRUE / FALSE

Signs of spring

How many of these things can you spot
in this springtime scene?

A young deer
10 patches of yellow primroses
Tree with pink blossom
Two blue butterflies
Five early purple orchids
Dangling catkin flowers in a tree
A blue tit with a caterpillar
A little wood mouse
Five rabbits

Buzzy bees

All kinds of busy bees buzz around gardens, collecting a sweet liquid, called nectar, from inside flowers. Some live in big groups; others on their own in tiny nests.

Honey bee nest

Honey bees live in huge nests with thousands of other bees. They turn the nectar they collect into honey, then store it in little cells inside their nests to feed to their young.

Bees in a nest do different jobs. Read the descriptions and study the nest here. Then see if you can answer these questions:

1. Which one is the queen bee? Circle her below.

2. What type of bee is A? ....

3. How many worker bees are there? ....

4. What is B? ....

5. And C? ....

Queen bee
Biggest bee in the hive. Lays eggs and is the mother of all bees in the hive.

Worker bees
Female bees that look after the hive, finding nectar and feeding young.

Larva
Young bees that look like squirmy white worms.

Pupa
When a larva is turning into a bee. Starts to grow a body, head and legs.

Drones
Male bees. Bigger than workers but smaller than the queen.

Waggle dance

When honey bees find flowers with lots of nectar, they do a series of movements, called a waggle dance, to tell the other bees where the flowers are. Read about the waggle dance, then match the descriptions of where the flowers are to the correct diagrams.

If the flowers are very close to the nest, the bee walks around in a circle.

If the flowers are further away, the bee walks in a loop swaying, or waggling, its body from side to side.

The more the bee waggles, the further away the flowers are.

If the bee waggles towards the Sun, the flowers are in the direction of the Sun. If it waggles away from the Sun, the flowers are in the opposite direction.

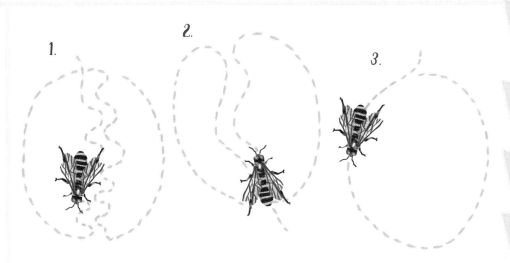

1.

2.

3.

A. 2m (6ft) from the hive, away from the Sun.

B. 100m (300ft) from the hive, towards the Sun.

C. 500m (1,600ft) from the hive, away from the Sun.

Bee homes

Different types of bees nest in different places. Look at the nests here. Four of them are bees' nests, but one ISN'T. Can you guess which it is?

Snail shell

Paper nest

Man-made hive

Old animal burrow

Hole in a fence post

71

Wild flowers

Colourful wild flowers grow in spring and summer, covering whole fields, meadows and hillsides. Bees, butterflies and other animals come to feed from them.

Missing colours

Look at the key and use it as a guide to colour in the different wild flowers on these pages.

Purple coneflower

Corn poppy

California poppy

Bluebonnet

Black-eyed Susan

Cornflower

Blanket flower

Daisy

Butterflies and other bugs

Add colour to the bugs flying around and feeding from the flowers too.

Swallowtail butterfly

Ladybird

Painted lady butterfly

Honey bee

Animal tracking

When people track animals, they're looking for clues that creatures have passed through or live nearby.

Animal clues

Can you spot any clues left by squirrels, badgers and thrushes in this scene?

Thrushes eat snails by smashing the shells on rocks. They lay speckled blue eggs. Their feathers are pale brown.

Badgers dig underground burrows called setts at the base of trees. They leave piles of droppings outside their setts. They sharpen their claws by scratching on tree trunks and fences.

Squirrels crack open hard nuts to eat the soft insides. They also chew the outsides of pine cones. Look for their footprints on muddy ground.

Footprints

The easiest way to track most animals is by looking for their footprints on muddy or snowy ground. Can you match the animals to their prints?

1. A **fox's** feet are very similar to a dog's.

2. Deer have two long, hard coverings, called hooves, on each foot.

3. Ducks have skin between their toes to help them swim.

4. A **rabbit's** back feet are very different from its front ones.

5. Mice are tiny. Their front and back feet have different claws.

The prints here are roughly the same size as in real life. But some would be too big to fit. For example, a grizzly bear's footprint would fill most of this page.

Answers & solutions

4-5 PARK PUZZLES

Animals to spot:

- ⬤ Squirrel eating a nut
- ◯ Yellow butterfly
- ◯ Coots
- ⬤ Mole
- ◯ Fox and cubs
- ◯ Bird and chicks
- ⬤ Raccoon

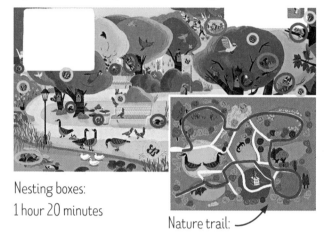

Nesting boxes:
1 hour 20 minutes

Nature trail:

6-7 EGGS AND NESTS

Which nest?: 1.B, 2.E, 3.D, 4.C, 5.A

Egg Sudoku:

Find the cuckoo's egg:
The cuckoo's egg is in this nest:

Are you an egghead?:
1. A koala doesn't lay eggs. 2. c) over 250,000. 3. TRUE

8-9 GARDEN BUGS

Slug trail:

Living underground:
Cockchafer: April 2016
Stag beetle: May 2012
Cicada: June 2001
Crane fly: September 2017

Bug trap:

10-11 BEAUTIFUL BEETLES

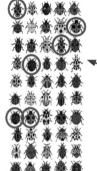

Ladybird spots:
The matching pairs are:

Largest, smallest:
1. Titan beetle, 2. Rhinoceros beetle,
3. Actaeon beetle, 4. Hercules beetle,
5. Giraffe stag beetle

12-15 IN THE POND

Pond dipping:

Stickleback babies:

6 are tadpoles.

Dashing dragonflies:
The matching one is C.

What is it?:
Common FROG, Green tree FROG, American TOAD,
Great crested NEWT, Natterjack TOAD

16-17 IT STARTS WITH A SEED

How does it grow?:

Seeds to plants:
1. Sunflower, 2. Pumpkin,
3. Poppy, 4. Apple,
5. Avocado, 6. Orange,
7. Sweet corn

How many grow?: 6

18-19 BUSY BORDER

Leafy bees:

Missing tags: Fern, Rosemary, Chives

Plant spotter:
1. Choisya, 2. Lamb's ear, 3. Sea holly, 4. Hosta

20-21 BY THE RIVER

Beaver pool: The river weed that will take them back home is highlighted:

The three creatures that DON'T live in a river are: cat, rabbit and squirrel.

Hungry otters:
1. WATER SNAIL, 2. CATFISH, 3. BULLFROG, 4. MAYFLY NYMPH, 5. BROWN TROUT, 6. CRAYFISH, 7. MUSSELS

Fish in hiding:

22-23 ANTS

Ant food: Grass seed: 4, Hawk moth: 2, European wasp: 1, Plum: 3

Ant carrying larva:

Which ant:
1. ACORN ANT 2. FIRE ANT
3. CARPENTER ANT
4. LEAF CUTTER ANT
5. COMMON BLACK ANT

Wood ant maze:

24-27 BIRD WATCHING

Flying birds:
1. Whooper swan, 2. Long-tailed tit, 3. Lapwing, 4. Red kite

Different jays:

Woodland birds:

 1. TAWNY OWL

2. WOOD PIGEON

 3. BLUE TIT

5. LONG TAILED TIT

4. TREE CREEPER

6. GREEN WOODPECKER

28-29 NATURE AT NIGHT

◯ Glowing fireflies   ⬤ Animal eyes

Many moths:

Luna moth: 23   Imperial moth: 19
Spotted hawkmoth: 23   Regal moth: 5
Sphinx moth: 10
The missing moth is the garden tiger moth.

Night animals: The two animals that ARE NOT awake at night are: carrion crow and adder

30-31 SNAKES AND LIZARDS

Hidden lizards:

Lizard or snake?
A horned viper is a SNAKE, Burton's LIZARD,
Garter SNAKE, Scarlet king SNAKE,
Burrowing SKINK (lizard), Glass LIZARD

How long?
A. 7–10am Corn snake, B. 2–3.30am Gila monster,
C. 9–9.45 European green lizard

34-35 IN THE WOODS

How old?: 1. 2003, 2: 2005, 3. 2008

Woodland quiz
1. d); 2. 1c), 2d), 3a), 4b); 3. b); 4. TRUE, 5. c) and e); 6. d)

36-39 ON THE SEASHORE

Seashore hunt:

◉ Abalone shell   ◯ Periwinkle shell
◯ Heart urchin shell   ◯ Scallop shell
◯ Driftwood   ◯ Bladderwrack seaweed
◯ Cuttlefish bone   ◯ Crab claw

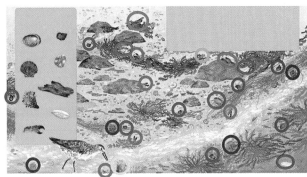

Tide puzzle:
The best day for the family to visit the beach is 14TH JULY.

Rock pool wordsearch:
SHORE CRAB isn't hidden in the wordsearch.

Before and after: The 15 differences are:

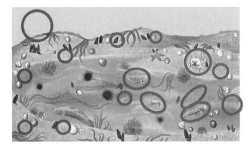

40-41 FLUTTERING BUTTERFLIES

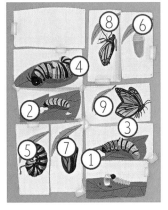

Caterpillar to butterfly:

42-45 AUTUMN

Changing scene:
The 18 differences are:

Nuts, fruits and seeds:
Cone 5, Helicopter seeds 1,
Rosehips 3, Acorns 2,
Elderberries 7,
Conkers 6, Sloes 4

46-47 AT THE NATURE RESERVE

Which reserve?:
Evie: Bare Hill
Alex: Big City Reserve
Oliver: Golden Woods
Saba: Little Bay Estuary

Reserve visitors:

48-49 ON THE MOVE

Journey map:
Mexican free-tailed bat: 23 days
Monarch butterfly: 38 days

Animal journeys:
Southern right whale: 5,000km/3,000 miles
Common toad: 1km/0.5 miles
European swallow: 16,000km/10,000 miles
Elk: 225km/140 miles

Swimming salmon: Other river creatures are circled.

50-51 AMAZING MUSHROOMS

Fungus knowledge: 1. b Penny bun, 2. a Honey fungus,
3. FALSE, 4. 1c, 2a, 3b, 5. TRUE

52-53 ANIMAL HOMES

Missing vowels:
RABBIT WARREN, BAT'S ROOST, BIRD'S NEST, BEEHIVE,
ANTHILL, FISH POND, SPIDER'S WEB, FOX'S DEN

Which home?
Eagle eyrie, squirrel
drey, beaver lodge,
bear den

Burrow maze:

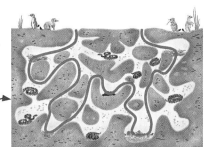

54-55 CLOUDY SKIES

1. Cirroculumus, fair but cold weather (it's winter)
2. Stratus, drizzle
3. Cumulonimbus, storm
4. Cumulus, storm (the clouds are getting bigger)

56-59 WINTER

Winter sky:

Bark match
A. Sequoia, B. Oak,
C. Plane, D. Sweet
chestnut, E. Birch

Footprints in the snow:
The rat footprint is missing from the jumble.

52-53 FOOD FOR EVERYONE

Storing food: The jay will find 9 acorns.

Which food?: 1.B, 2.C, 3.A, 4.E, 5.D.

Picking over pellets:
Crow: wheat, fish, ground beetle, vole
Short-eared owl: vole, mouse
Herring gull: fish, clam, ground beetle
Blackbird: millipedes, damson, wheat
Buzzard: ground beetle, mouse, dry grass, vole

62-65 AT SEA

Lounging seals: There are 32 adults and 14 seal pups.

Sea forecast: The
best day to visit the
island is 11TH MAY.

Hungry puffins:

Sea creature spiral:
SEAL, PARROTFISH, CLOWNFISH, SEASLUG, DOLPHIN,
OCTOPUS, HERMIT CRAB, CONCH, JELLYFISH, SEA TURTLE,
CUTTLEFISH, SAND EEL, SQUID, GIANT CLAM, NAUTILUS

Turtle generations: 24 turtle babies

Coral reefs:

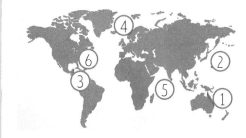

Match the corals:

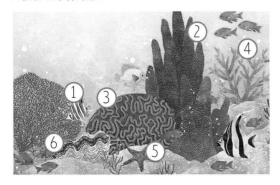

66-67 SPIDERS

Magic markings:

1. Black widow
2. Garden spider
3. Jumping spider
4. Red-knee tarantula
5. Wasp spider

Spider true or false: The air spider isn't a real spider.

Wonderful webs: 1. Green-fanged spider, 2. False widow,
3. Hammock-weaver, 4. Marbled orb weaver
The wolf spider hasn't made a web.

Spider food:

Oak tree moth: B
House fly: E
Green bottle fly: D
Cockroach: A
Sawfly: C

68-69 SPRINGTIME

Baby animals:
1. CHICK, 2. FOAL, 3. PUP, 4. CUB, 5. LAMB, 6. FAWN

True or false:
1. False, 2. True, 3. True, 4. False, 5. True, 6. False

Signs of spring:

- Young deer
- Blue butterfly
- Early purple orchid
- Blue tit with caterpillar
- Rabbit
- Yellow primrose
- Pink blossom
- Catkins
- Wood mouse

70-71 BUZZY BEES

Honey bee nest:

1.
2. Drone
3. 32
4. Larva
5. Pupa

Waggle dance: 3A, 2B, 1C

Bee homes:
The paper nest isn't a home for bees, it's a wasp's nest.

74-75 ANIMAL TRACKING

Animal clues: Here are the signs of:

- Thrush
- Badger
- Squirrel

Footprints:

Additional illustration by Gemma Capdevila and Florence Weiser   Cover illustration by Gemma Capdevila
Managing designer: Zoe Wray   Series editor: Jane Chisholm   Digital manipulation by John Russell   Nature consultant: Zoë Simmons